Alice thought to herself.
"I don't see how he
can *ever* finish, if he doesn't
begin." But she waited
patiently.

*Wonderland, Chapter 9*

First published 1997 by Macmillan Children's Books
a division of Macmillan Publishers Limited
25 Eccleston Place, London SW1W 9NF
and Basingstoke
Associated companies throughout the world

ISBN 0 333 68625 2

Illustrations coloured by Harry Theaker
copyright © 1911 Macmillan Publishers Limited
Illustrations coloured by Diz Wallis, represented by Folio,
copyright © 1995 and 1996 Macmillan Publishers Limited
All rights reserved.

The right of Diz Wallis to be identified as the
colourist of images in this work has been
asserted by her in accordance with
the Copyright, Designs and Patents Act 1988.

1 3 5 7 9 8 6 4 2

A CIP catalogue record for this book is available
from the British Library.

Printed in Singapore

# "Curiouser and Curiouser!"

*Quotations from* Alice's Adventures in Wonderland
*and* Through the Looking-Glass

by Lewis Carroll

with illustrations by Sir John Tenniel

MACMILLAN

"Curiouser and curiouser!" cried Alice (she was so much surprised, that for the moment she quite forgot how to speak good English.)

*Wonderland, Chapter 2*

# Contents

"Oh, I've had such a curious dream!" said Alice.

*Identity Crises*

# "I don't like belonging to another person's dream."

Looking-Glass, Chapter 8

"If that there King was to wake," added
Tweedledum,
"you'd go out
—bang!—
just like
a candle!"

*Looking-Glass,*
*Chapter 4*

"Speak in French when you can't think of the
English for a thing—turn out your toes as
you walk—and remember who you are!"

*Looking-Glass, Chapter 2*

"I am real!" said Alice, and began to cry.
"You won't make yourself a bit realler by
crying," Tweedledee remarked: "there's nothing
to cry about."

*Looking-Glass, Chapter 4*

"Who are *you*?" said the Caterpillar.
This was not an encouraging opening
for a conversation.

*Wonderland, Chapter 5*

"I can't explain *myself*, I'm afraid, Sir," said Alice,
"because I'm not myself, you see."

*Wonderland, Chapter 5*

"How do you know I'm mad?" said Alice.
"You must be," said the Cat, "or you
wouldn't have come here."

*Wonderland, Chapter 10*

"My name means the shape I am—and a good handsome shape it is, too." . . . "With a name like yours, you might be any shape, almost."

*Looking-Glass, Chapter 6*

"I—I'm a little girl," said Alice, rather doubtfully, as she remembered the number of changes she had gone through that day.

*Wonderland, Chapter 5*

"Are you a child or a teetotum?" the Sheep said, as she took up another pair of needles.

*Looking-Glass, Chapter 5*

"What's the use of their having names," the Gnat said, "if they won't answer to them?"

*Looking-Glass, Chapter 3*

The Lion looked at Alice wearily. "Are you an animal or vegetable—or mineral?" he said.

*Looking-Glass, Chapter 7*

"I suppose you don't want to lose your name?" "No, indeed," Alice said, a little anxiously.

*Looking-Glass, Chapter 3*

"I shouldn't know you again if we *did* meet . . . you're so exactly like other people."

*Looking-Glass, Chapter 6*

"Well! *What* are you?" said the Pigeon. "I can see you're trying to invent something!"

*Wonderland, Chapter 5*

"Well, now that we have seen each other," said the Unicorn, "if you'll believe in me, I'll believe in you. Is that a bargain?"

*Looking-Glass, Chapter 7*

This time she found a little bottle . . .
with the words "DRINK ME"
beautifully printed on it in large letters.

*Wonderland, Chapter 5*

# Growing and Shrinking

# "Good-bye feet!"

Wonderland, Chapter 2

"It was much pleasanter at home," thought poor Alice, "when one wasn't always growing larger and smaller, and being ordered about by mice and rabbits."

*Wonderland, Chapter 4*

"I can't help it," said Alice very meekly: "I'm growing."

"You've no right to grow here," said the Dormouse.

*Wonderland, Chapter 11*

"Oh how I wish I could shut up like a telescope! I think I could, if I only knew how to begin."

*Wonderland, Chapter 1*

It was so long since she had been anything near the right size, that it felt quite strange at first.

*Wonderland, Chapter 5*

"It's as large as life and twice as natural!"

*Looking-Glass, Chapter 7*

"Good-bye feet!" (for when she looked down at her feet, they seemed to be almost out of sight).

*Wonderland, Chapter 2*

"I never ask advice about growing," Alice said indignantly.

*Looking-Glass, Chapter 6*

"In my youth," Father William replied to his son,
    "I feared it might injure the brain;
But, now that I'm perfectly sure I have none,
    Why, I do it again and again."

Looking-Glass, Chapter 8

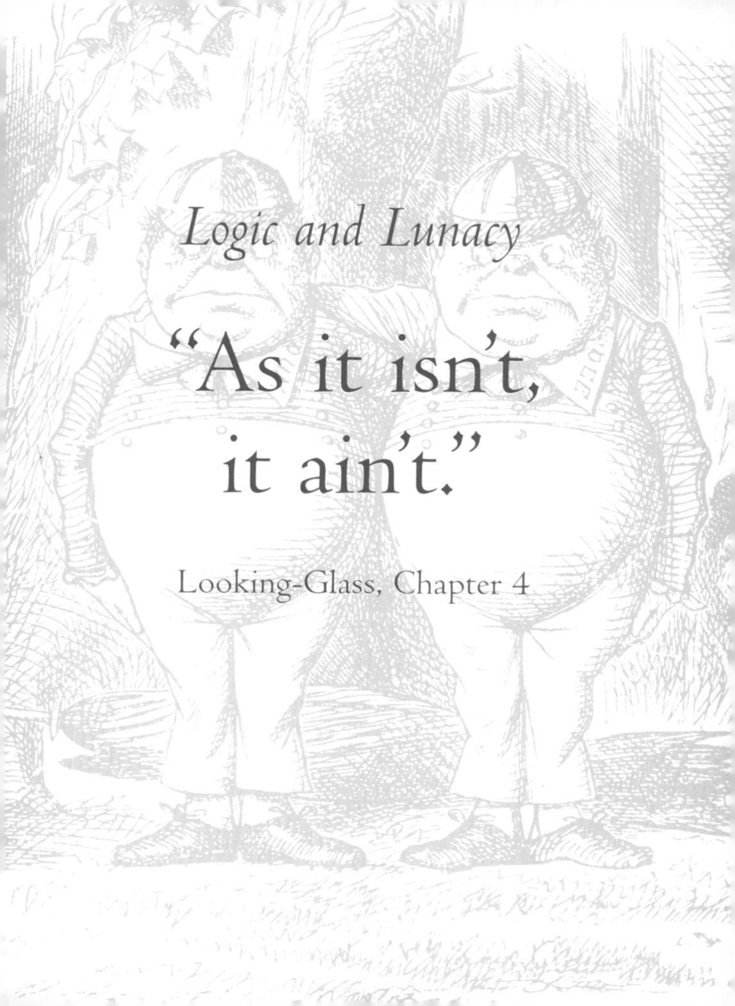

*Logic and Lunacy*

# "As it isn't, it ain't."

Looking-Glass, Chapter 4

"Let the jury consider their verdict," the King said . . .

"No, no!" said the Queen. "Sentence first —verdict afterwards."

*Wonderland, Chapter 12*

"If it was so, it might be; and if it were so, it would be; but as it isn't, it ain't. That's logic."

*Looking-Glass, Chapter 4*

"You have baked me too brown, I must sugar my hair."

*Wonderland, Chapter 10*

"Can you do Division? Divide a loaf by a knife—what's the answer to *that?*"

*Looking-Glass, Chapter 9*

"Now the reason hair falls off is because it hangs *down*—things never fall *upwards*, you know."

*Looking-Glass, Chapter 8*

"But I was thinking of a plan
    To dye one's whiskers green,
And always use so large a fan
    That they could not be seen."

*Looking-Glass, Chapter 8*

"How am I to get in?" asked Alice again, in a louder tone.

"*Are* you to get in at all?" said the Footman. "That's the first question, you know."

*Wonderland, Chapter 6*

"There's a large mustard-mine near here. And the moral of that is—'The more there is of mine, the less there is of yours'."

*Wonderland*, Chapter 9

"Take off your hat," the King said to the Hatter.

"It isn't mine," said the Hatter.

"*Stolen!*" the King exclaimed.

*Wonderland*, Chapter 11

"I don't deny things with my *hands*," Alice objected.

"Nobody said you did," said the Red Queen, "I said you couldn't if you tried."

*Looking-Glass*, Chapter 9

The King's argument was that anything that had a head could be beheaded, and that you weren't to talk nonsense.

*Wonderland, Chapter 8*

"No wise fish would go anywhere without a porpoise."

*Wonderland, Chapter 10*

"I can't go no lower," said the Hatter: "I'm on the floor, as it is."

*Wonderland, Chapter 11*

"Try another Subtraction sum. Take a bone from a dog: what remains?"

*Looking-Glass, Chapter 9*

"'Be what you would seem to be'—or, if you'd like it put more simply—'Never imagine yourself not to be otherwise than what it might appear to others that what you were or might have been was not otherwise than what you had been would have appeared to them to be otherwise.'"

*Wonderland, Chapter 9*

"Never mind what they all say, my dear, but take a return-ticket every time the train stops."

*Looking-Glass, Chapter 3*

"She ought to know her way to the ticket-office, even if she doesn't know her alphabet!"

*Looking-Glass, Chapter 3*

"*And now, if e'er by chance I put
My fingers into glue,
Or madly squeeze a right-hand foot
Into a left-hand shoe . . .*"

*Looking-Glass, Chapter 8*

"*The other Messenger's called Hatta. I must
have* two, *you know—to come and go. One
to come, and one to go.*"

*Looking-Glass, Chapter 7*

$A$nd as in uffish thought he stood
The Jabberwock, with eyes of flame,
Came whiffling through the tulgey wood,
And burbled as it came!

*Looking-Glass, Chapter 1*

# Curious Creatures

# "The frumious Bandersnatch!"

Looking-Glass, Chapter 1

"**B**eware the Jabberwock, my son!
The jaws that bite, the claws that catch!
Beware the Jubjub bird, and shun
The frumious Bandersnatch!"

*Looking-Glass, Chapter 1*

"**M**ine is a long and a sad tale!"
said the Mouse . . .

"It *is* a long
tail, certainly,"
said Alice . . .
"but why do
you call it sad?"

*Wonderland, Chapter 3*

"**O**nce," said the Mock Turtle at last, with a
deep sigh, "I was a real Turtle."

*Wonderland, Chapter 9*

"I didn't know that Cheshire-Cats always grinned; in fact, I didn't know that cats *could* grin."
    "They all can," said the Duchess; "and most of 'em do."

*Wonderland, Chapter 6*

"Flamingoes and mustard both bite. And the moral of that is—'Birds of a feather flock together.'"

*Wonderland, Chapter 9*

"*Will you walk a little faster?*" *said a whiting to a snail,*
    "*There's a porpoise close behind us, and he's treading on my tail.*"

*Wonderland, Chapter 10*

"Where are you going? Look up, speak nicely, and don't twiddle your fingers all the time."

*Looking-Glass, Chapter 2*

*Rudeness and Manners*

# "You're enough to try the patience of an oyster!"

Wonderland, Chapter 3

"Really, now you ask me," said Alice, very much confused, "I don't think——"

"Then you shouldn't talk," said the Hatter. This piece of rudeness was more than Alice could bear.

*Wonderland, Chapter 7*

"Don't grunt," said Alice; "that's not at all a proper way of expressing yourself."

*Wonderland, Chapter 6*

"A little kindness—and putting her hair in papers—would do wonders with her——"

*Looking-Glass, Chapter 9*

"**Y**ou should learn not to make personal remarks," Alice said with some severity: "it's very rude."

*Wonderland, Chapter 7*

"**W**ho cares for *you?*" said Alice (she had grown to her full size by this time). "You're nothing but a pack of cards!"

*Wonderland, Chapter 12*

**S**he generally gave herself very good advice (though she very seldom followed it), and sometimes she scolded herself so severely as to bring tears into her eyes.

*Wonderland, Chapter 1*

"Speak roughly to your little boy,
   And beat him when he sneezes;
He only does it to annoy,
   Because he knows it teases.

*Wonderland, Chapter 6*

"If you think we're waxworks, you ought to pay,
you know.
Waxworks
weren't made
to be looked
at for nothing.
Nohow!"

*Looking-Glass,
Chapter 4*

"I beg your pardon?" said Alice.
   "It isn't respectable to beg," said the King.

*Looking-Glass, Chapter 7*

"'I have answered three questions, and that is enough,'
Said his father; 'don't give yourself airs!
Do you think I can listen all day to such stuff?
Be off, or I'll kick you downstairs!'"

*Wonderland, Chapter 5*

"Consider what a great girl you are . . .
Consider what o'clock it is.
Consider anything, only
don't cry!"

*Looking-Glass, Chapter 6*

"If you're going to
turn into a pig, my
dear," said Alice,
seriously, "I'll have
nothing more to do
with you."

*Wonderland, Chapter 5*

"May I give you a slice?" [Alice] said.

"Certainly not," the Red Queen said, very decidedly: "It isn't etiquette to cut any one you've been introduced to. Remove the joint!"

*Looking-Glass, Chapter 9*

"Pudding—Alice; Alice—Pudding. Remove the pudding!" and the waiters took it away so quickly that Alice couldn't return its bow.

*Looking-Glass, Chapter 9*

Stooping down to the daisies, who were just beginning again, she whispered, "If you don't hold your tongues, I'll pick you!"

*Looking-Glass, Chapter 2*

"Curtesy while you're thinking what to say.
It saves time."

*Looking-Glass, Chapter 2*

"It's time for you to answer now," the Queen
said, looking at her watch: "open your mouth
a *little* wider when you speak, and always say,
'your Majesty'."

*Looking-Glass, Chapter 2*

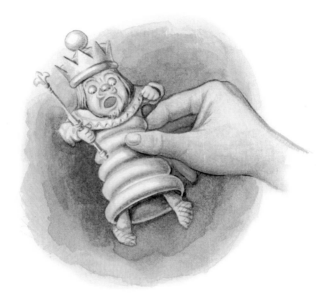

"I assure you, my dear, I turned cold to the very ends of my whiskers!"

Looking-Glass, Chapter 1

# "Of cabbages——
and kings——"

## and Queens

Looking-Glass, Chapter 4

"How fast those Queens can run!"

*Looking-Glass, Chapter 7*

"It'll never do for you to be lolling about on the grass like that! Queens have to be dignified, you know!"

*Looking-Glass, Chapter 9*

"Imperial fiddlestick!" said the King.

*Looking-Glass, Chapter 1*

"Queens never make bargains."

*Looking-Glass, Chapter 9*

" 'The time has come,' the Walrus said,
'To talk of many things:
Of shoes—and ships—and sealing-wax—
Of cabbages—and kings—
And why the sea is boiling hot—
And whether pigs have wings.'"

*Looking-Glass, Chapter 4*

"Some people," said Humpty Dumpty . . .
"have no more sense than a baby!"

*Looking-Glass, Chapter 6*

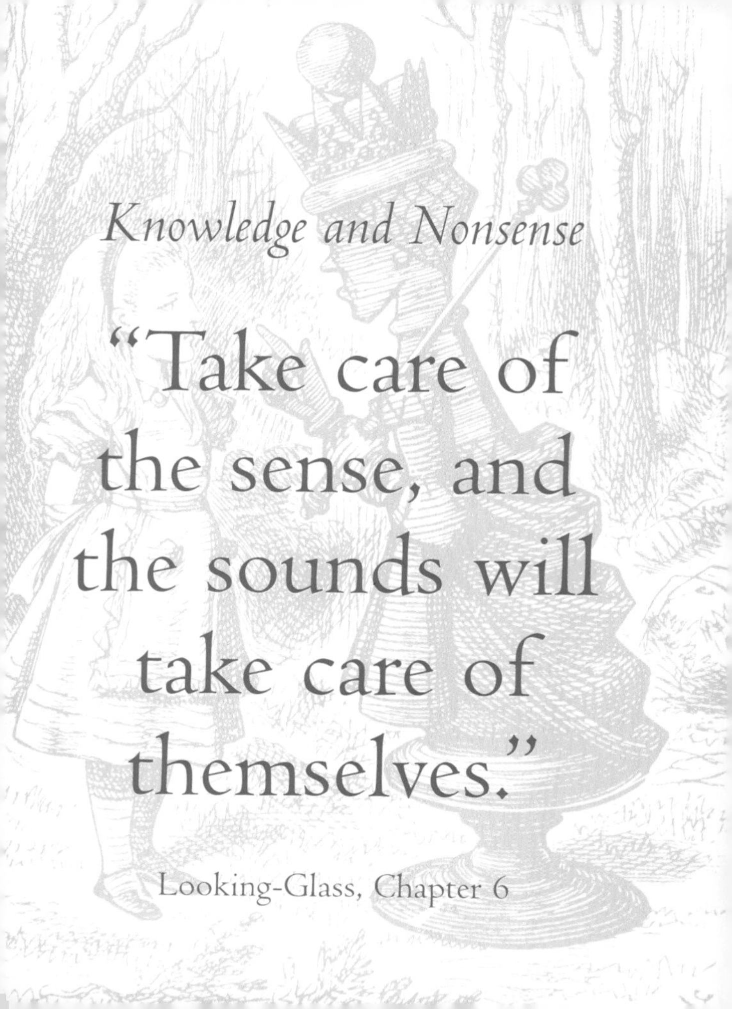

*Knowledge and Nonsense*

# "Take care of the sense, and the sounds will take care of themselves."

Looking-Glass, Chapter 6

"That's the reason they're called lessons," the Gryphon remarked: "because they lessen from day to day."

*Wonderland, Chapter 9*

"We called him Tortoise because he taught us," said the Mock Turtle.

*Wonderland, Chapter 9*

"Why, sometimes I've believed as many as six impossible things before breakfast."

*Looking-Glass, Chapter 5*

"Always speak the truth—think before you speak—and write it down afterwards."

*Looking-Glass, Chapter 9*

Alice had not the slightest idea what Latitude was, or Longitude either, but she thought they were nice grand words to say.

*Wonderland, Chapter 1*

"What is the use of a book," thought Alice, "without pictures or conversations?"

*Wonderland, Chapter 1*

"I don't know the meaning of half those long words, and, what's more, I don't believe you do either!"

*Wonderland, Chapter 3*

"Arithmetic—Ambition, Distraction, Uglification and Derision."

*Wonderland, Chapter 9*

"Then you should say what you mean," the March Hare went on.

"I do," Alice hastily replied; "at least—at least I mean what I say—that's the same thing, you know."

"Not the same thing a bit!" said the Hatter. "Why, you might just as well say that 'I see what I eat' is the same thing as 'I eat what I see'!"

*Wonderland, Chapter 7*

"What's the French for fiddle-de-dee?"

"Fiddle-de-dee's not English," Alice replied.

*Looking-Glass, Chapter 9*

"You see it's like a portmanteau—there are two meanings packed up into one word."

*Looking-Glass, Chapter 6*

"If there's no meaning in it," said the King, "that saves a world of trouble, you know, as we needn't try to find any."

*Wonderland, Chapter 12*

The Red Queen shook her head. "You may call it 'nonsense' if you like," she said, "but I've heard nonsense, compared with which that would be as sensible as a dictionary!"

*Looking-Glass, Chapter 2*

"This conversation is going on a little too fast: let's go back to the last remark but one."

*Looking-Glass, Chapter 6*

"Four times five is twelve, and four times six is thirteen, and four times seven is— oh dear! I shall never get to twenty at that rate!"

*Wonderland, Chapter 2*

"You don't know much," said the Duchess; "and that's a fact."

*Wonderland, Chapter 6*

"The Drawling-master was an old conger-eel . . . *he* taught us Drawling, Stretching and Fainting in Coils."

*Wonderland, Chapter 9*

"When I make a word do a lot of work like that," said Humpty Dumpty, "I always pay it extra."

*Looking-Glass, Chapter 6*

"I can read words of one letter! Isn't *that* grand? However, don't be discouraged. You'll come to it in time."

*Looking-Glass, Chapter 9*

"Fan her head!" the Red Queen anxiously interrupted. "She'll be feverish after so much thinking."

*Looking-Glass, Chapter 9*

"From the Queen. An invitation for the
Duchess to play croquet."

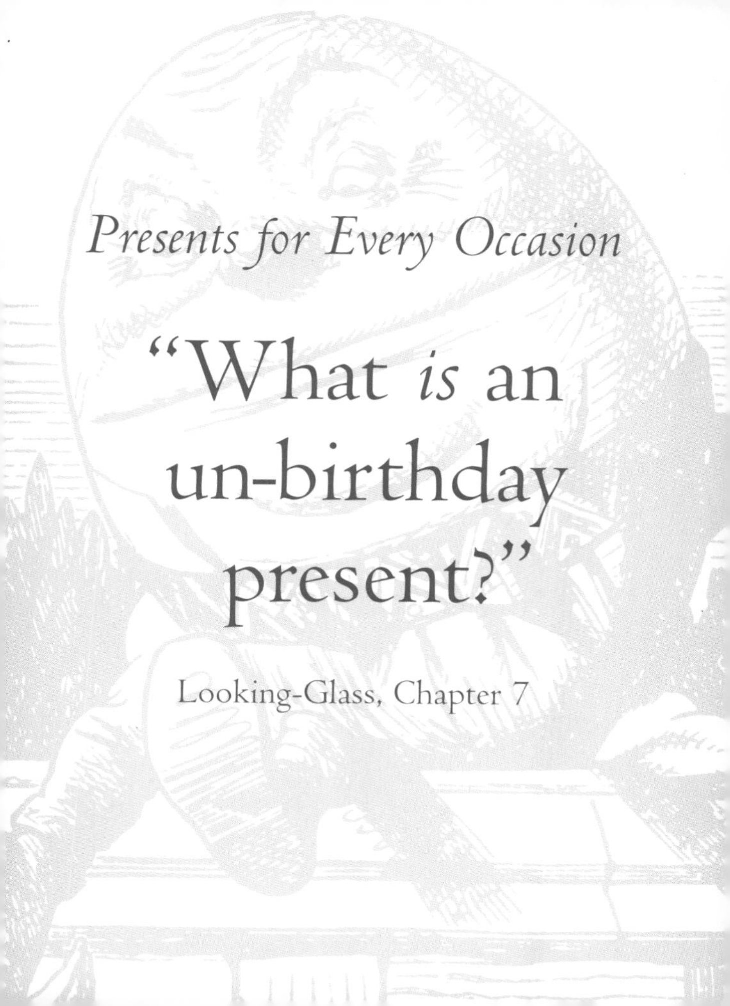

*Presents for Every Occasion*

# "What *is* an un-birthday present?"

Looking-Glass, Chapter 7

"How funny it'll seem, sending presents to one's own feet! And how odd the directions will look!

*Alice's Right Foot, Esq.,*
*Hearthrug,*
*near the Fender,*
*(with Alice's love).*

*Wonderland, Chapter 2*

"I make you a present of everything I've said as yet."

"A cheap sort of present!" thought Alice. "I'm glad they don't give birthday-presents like that!"

*Wonderland, Chapter 9*

"What *is* an un-birthday present?"
"A present given when it isn't your birthday, of course."

*Looking-Glass, Chapter 6*

The Dodo solemnly presented the thimble, saying, "We beg your acceptance of this elegant thimble."

*Wonderland, Chapter 3*

*I* gave her one, they gave him two,
  You gave us three or more;
They all returned from him to you,
  Though they were mine before.

*Wonderland, Chapter 12*

"Another sandwich!" said the King;
"There's nothing but hay left now,"
the Messenger said, peeping into the bag.

"Hay, then," the King murmured in a
faint whisper.

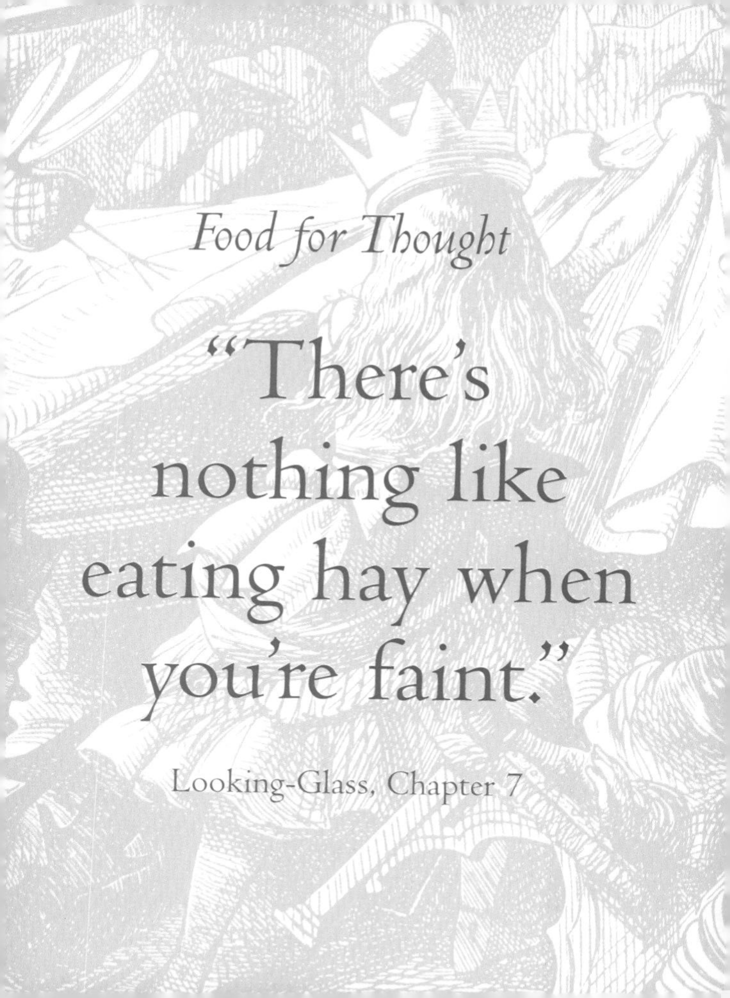

*Food for Thought*

# "There's nothing like eating hay when you're faint."

Looking-Glass, Chapter 7

She opened it, and found in it a very small cake, on which the words "EAT ME" were beautifully marked in currants.

*Wonderland, Chapter 1*

She had never forgotten that, if you drink from a bottle marked "poison", it is almost certain to disagree with you, sooner or later.

*Wonderland, Chapter 1*

"Two days wrong!" sighed the Hatter. "I told you butter wouldn't suit the works!"

*Wonderland, Chapter 7*

"You look a little shy: let me introduce you to that leg of mutton," said the Red Queen.

*Looking-Glass, Chapter 9*

"Put cats in the coffee, and mice in the tea—
And welcome Queen Alice with thirty-times-three!"

*Looking-Glass, Chapter 9*

"Now the cleverest thing that I ever did," he went on after a pause, "was inventing a new pudding during the meat-course."

*Looking-Glass, Chapter 8*

"Come, fetch out the plum-cake, old man!" the Unicorn went on, turning from [Alice] to the King. "None of your brown bread for me!"

*Looking-Glass, Chapter 7*

"You don't know how to manage Looking-glass cakes," the Unicorn remarked. "Hand it round first, and cut it afterwards."

*Looking-Glass, Chapter 7*

"When *I'm* a Duchess," she said to herself (not in a very hopeful tone, though) "I won't have any pepper in my kitchen at *all*. Soup does very well without . . ."

*Wonderland, Chapter 9*

"But answer came there none—
And this was scarcely odd, because
They'd eaten every one."

*Looking-Glass, Chapter 4*

◆ 61 ◆

"*Beautiful Soup, so rich and green,*
*Waiting in a hot tureen!*
*Who for such dainties would not stoop?*
*Soup of the evening, beautiful Soup!*"

*Wonderland, Chapter 10*

"You alarm me!" said the King. "I feel
faint—Give me a ham sandwich!"

*Looking-Glass, Chapter 7*

It had, in fact, a sort
of mixed flavour of
cherry-tart, custard,
pine-apple, roast
turkey, toffy, and hot
buttered toast [and]
she very soon finished
it off.

*Wonderland, Chapter 1*

"He said, 'I look for butterflies
    That sleep among the wheat:
I make them into mutton pies,
    And sell them in the street.'"

*Looking-Glass, Chapter 8*

"Take some more tea," the March Hare said
    to Alice, very earnestly.

"I've had nothing yet," Alice replied in an
offended tone, "so I can't take more."

*Wonderland, Chapter 7*

"What sort of things do *you* remember
best?" Alice ventured to ask.

"Oh, things that happened the week after
next," the Queen replied in a careless tone.

*Looking-Glass, Chapter 5*

*Difficult Directions*

# "That's the effect of living backwards."

Looking-Glass, Chapter 5

"You may look in front of you, and on both sides, if you like," said the Sheep; "but you can't look *all* round you—unless you've got eyes at the back of your head."

*Looking-Glass, Chapter 5*

"Would you tell me, please, which way I ought to go from here?"

"That depends a good deal on where you want to get to," said the Cat.

"I don't much care where——" said Alice.

"Then it doesn't matter which way you go," said the Cat.

*Wonderland, Chapter 6*

"I'm sure nobody walks much faster than I do!"

"He can't do that," said the King, "or else he'd have been here first."

*Looking-Glass, Chapter 7*

"That's the effect of living backwards," the Queen said kindly: "it always makes one a little giddy at first—"

*Looking-Glass, Chapter 5*

"Well in *our* country," said Alice, still panting a little, "you'd generally get to somewhere else—if you ran very fast for a long time, as we've been doing."

"A slow sort of country!" said the Queen.

*Looking-Glass, Chapter 2*

In another moment Alice was through
the glass, and had jumped lightly
down into the Looking-glass room.

*Looking-Glass, Chapter 1*

*Strange and Unaccountable
Goings-on*

# "Curiouser and curiouser!"

Wonderland, Chapter 2

"Curiouser and curiouser!" cried Alice (she was so much surprised, that for the moment she quite forgot how to speak good English).

*Wonderland, Chapter 2*

"'You are old, Father William,' the young man said,
  'And your hair has become very white;
And yet you incessantly stand on your head—
  Do you think, at your age, it is right?'"

*Wonderland, Chapter 5*

"If you knew Time as well as I do," said the Hatter, "you wouldn't talk about wasting *it*. It's *him*."

*Wonderland, Chapter 7*

"He's an Anglo-Saxon Messenger—and those are Anglo-Saxon attitudes."

*Looking-Glass, Chapter 7*

"Did you ever see such a thing as a drawing of a muchness?"

*Wonderland, Chapter 7*

The last time she saw them, they were trying to put the Dormouse into the teapot.

*Wonderland, Chapter 7*

"We *can* talk," said the Tigerlily: "when there's anybody worth talking to."

*Looking-Glass, Chapter 2*

"In most gardens," the Tiger-lily said, "they make the beds too soft—so that the flowers are always asleep."

*Looking-Glass, Chapter 2*

It flashed across her mind that she had never before seen a rabbit with either a waistcoat-pocket, or a watch to take out of it.

*Wonderland, Chapter 1*

"Oh, I liked it well enough . . . only it *was* so dusty and hot, and the elephants *did* tease so!"

*Looking-Glass, Chapter 3*

'Twas brillig, and the slithy toves
    Did gyre and gimble in the wabe;
All mimsy were the borogoves,
    And the mome raths outgrabe.

*Looking-Glass, Chapter 1*

> "'*Twinkle, twinkle, little bat!*
> *How I wonder what you're at!*
> *Up above the world you fly,*
> *Like a tea-tray in the sky.*'"
>
> *Wonderland, Chapter 7*

"Well, then," the Cat went on, "you see a dog growls when it's angry, and wags its tail when it's pleased. Now I growl when I'm pleased, and wag my tail when I'm angry. Therefore I'm mad."

*Wonderland, Chapter 6*

In his confusion he bit a large piece out of his teacup instead of the bread-and-butter.

*Wonderland, Chapter 11*

*"The sun was shining on the sea,*
*Shining with all his might:*
*He did his very best to make*
*The billows smooth and bright—*
*And this was odd, because it was*
*The middle of the night."*

*Looking-Glass, Chapter 4*

"Well! I've often seen a cat without a grin,"
thought Alice; "but a grin without a cat!
It's the most curious thing I ever saw in my life!"

*Wonderland, Chapter 6*

T he King . . . read out from his book, "Rule Forty-Two. *All persons more than a mile high to leave the court.*"

*Wonderland, Chapter 12*

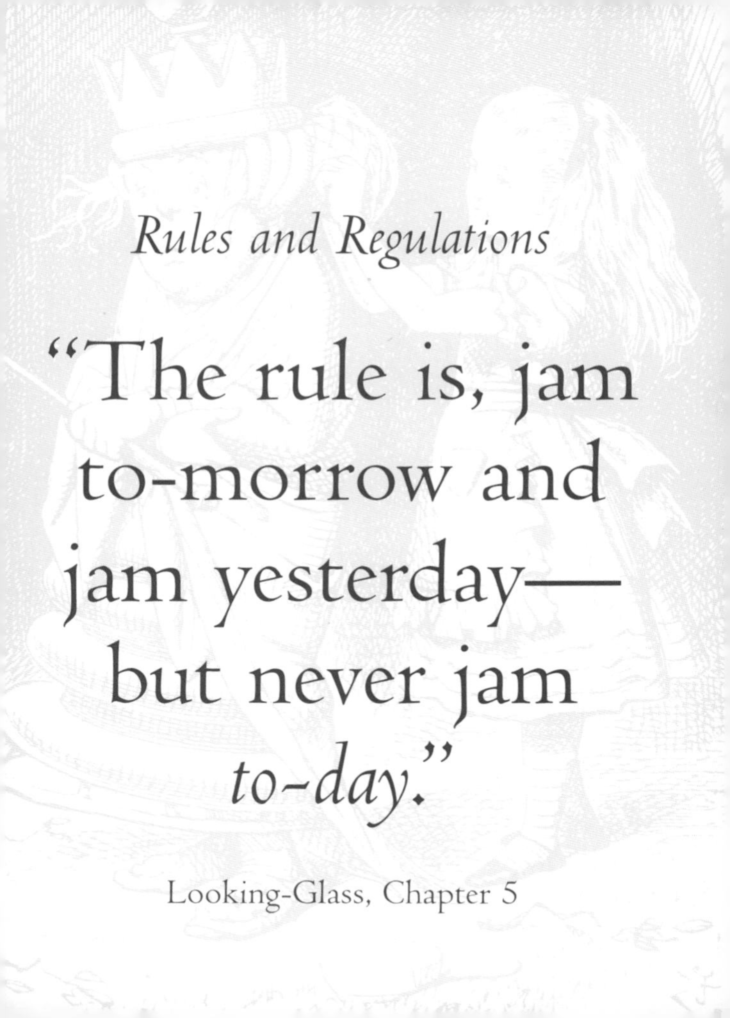

*Rules and Regulations*

# "The rule is, jam to-morrow and jam yesterday— but never jam *to-day.*"

Looking-Glass, Chapter 5

"Speak when you're spoken to!" the Queen sharply interrupted her.

"But if everybody obeyed that rule," said

Alice . . . "and if you only spoke when you were spoken to, and the other person always waited for *you* to begin, you see nobody would ever say anything . . ."

*Looking-Glass, Chapter 9*

"It's the oldest rule in the book," said the King. "Then it ought to be Number One," said Alice.

*Wonderland, Chapter 12*

"I wish *I* could manage to be glad!" the Queen said. "Only I never can remember the rule."

*Looking-Glass, Chapter 5*

"One rule seems to be, that if one Knight hits the other, he knocks him off his horse; and, if he misses, he tumbles off himself."

*Looking-Glass, Chapter 8*

Another Rule of Battle, that Alice had not noticed, seemed to be that they always fell on their heads.

*Looking-Glass, Chapter 8*

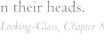

"It must come sometimes to 'jam to-day'," Alice objected.

"No, it can't," said the Queen. "It's jam every *other* day: to-day isn't any *other* day, you know."

*Looking-Glass, Chapter 5*

"Are their heads off?" shouted the Queen.

*Wonderland, Chapter 8*

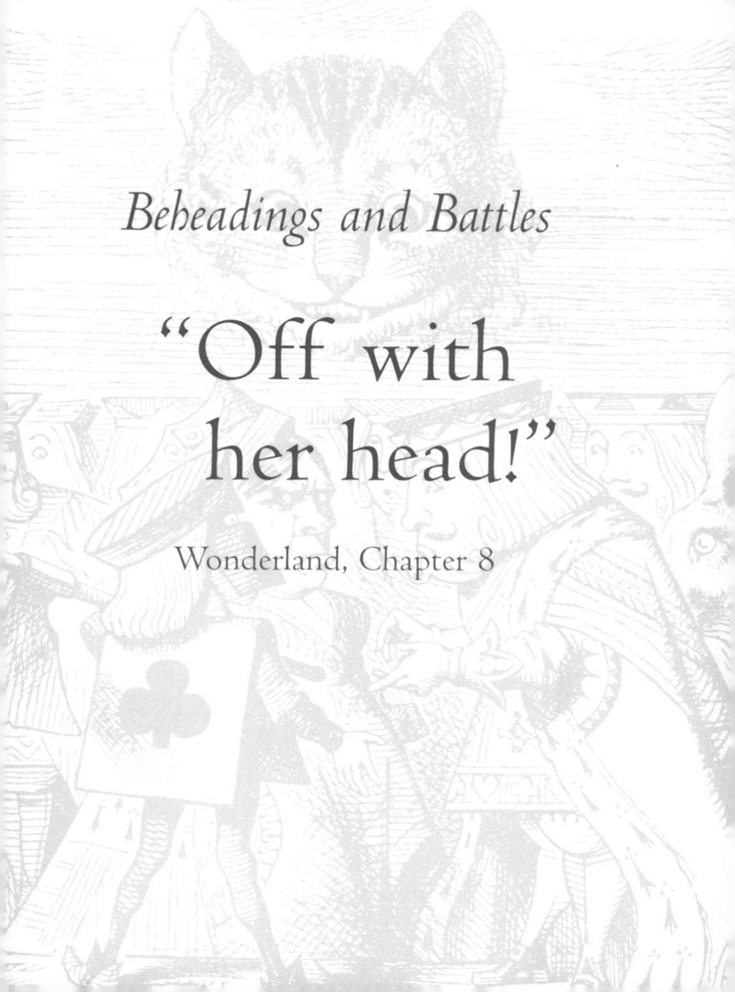

*Beheadings and Battles*

# "Off with her head!"

Wonderland, Chapter 8

"You see the earth takes twenty-four hours to turn on its axis——"

"Talking of axes," said the Duchess, "chop off her head!"

*Wonderland, Chapter 6*

"The Duchess! The Duchess! Oh my dear paws! Oh my fur and whiskers! She'll get me executed, as sure as ferrets are ferrets!"

*Wonderland, Chapter 4*

"Now, I give you fair warning," shouted the Queen, stamping on the ground as she spoke; "either you or your head must be off, and that in about half no time! Take your choice!"

*Wonderland, Chapter 9*

"If you do such a thing again, I'll have you buttered!"

*Looking-Glass, Chapter 7*

"Give your evidence," said the King; "and don't be nervous, or I'll have you executed on the spot."

This did not seem to encourage the witness at all.

*Wonderland, Chapter 11*

*"I cried, 'Come, tell me how you live!'*
*And thumped him on the head."*

*Looking-Glass, Chapter 8*

There was a pause in the fight just then, and the Lion and the Unicorn sat down, panting, while the King called out, "Ten minutes for refreshments!"

*Looking-Glass, Chapter 7*

"You know," he added gravely, "it's one of the most serious

things that can possibly happen to one in a battle—to get one's head cut off."

*Looking-Glass, Chapter 4*

"The Queen bawled out 'He's murdering the time! Off with his head!'"

*Wonderland, Chapter 7*

"I'm very brave generally," he went on in a low voice: "only to-day I happen to have a headache."

*Looking-Glass, Chapter 4*

One, two! One, two! And through and through
    The vorpal blade went snicker-snack!
He left it dead, and with its head
    He went galumphing back.

*Looking-Glass, Chapter 1*

"Fury said to
a mouse, That
he met in the
house, 'Let
us both go
to law: *I*
will prose-
cute *you.*—
Come, I'll
take no de-
nial; We
must have
the trial;
For really
this morn-
ing I've
nothing
to do.'
Said the
mouse to
the cur,
'Such a
trial, dear
sir, With
no jury
or judge,
would
be wast-
ing our
breath.'
'I'll be
judge,
I'll be
jury,'
said
cun-
ning
old
Fury:
'I'll
try
the
whole
cause
and
con-
demn
you to
death'."

*Wonderland, Chapter 3*

◆ 86 ◆

"Collar that Dormouse!" the Queen shrieked out. "Behead that Dormouse! Turn that Dormouse out of court! Suppress him! Pinch him! Off with his whiskers!"

*Wonderland, Chapter 11*

"They're dreadfully fond of beheading people here: the great wonder is that there's anyone left alive!"

*Wonderland, Chapter 8*

"Let's fight till six, and then have dinner," said Tweedledum.

*Looking-Glass, Chapter 4*

"Perhaps you were never even introduced to a
lobster . . . so you can have no idea what a
delightful thing a Lobster-Quadrille is?"

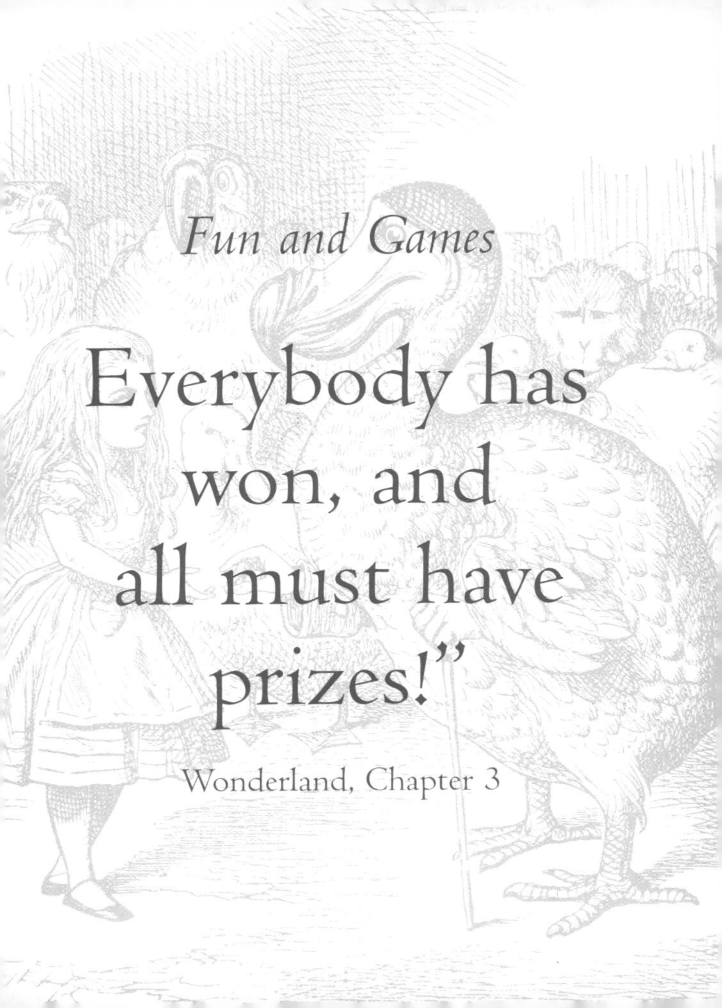

*Fun and Games*

# Everybody has won, and all must have prizes!"

Wonderland, Chapter 3

"Let's pretend the glass has got soft like gauze so that we can get through."

*Looking-Glass, Chapter 1*

The chief difficulty Alice found at first was in managing her flamingo.

*Wonderland, Chapter 8*

"Four times round is enough for one dance," Tweedledum panted . . .

*Looking-Glass, Chapter 4*

"Will you, won't you, will you, won't you, will you join the dance?
Will you, won't you, will you, won't you, won't you join the dance?"

*Wonderland, Chapter 10*

"I can repeat poetry as well as other folk if it comes to that—"

"Oh, it needn't come to that!" Alice hastily said.

*Looking-Glass, Chapter 6*

"I think you might do something better with the time," [Alice] said, "than wasting it in asking riddles that have no answers."

*Wonderland, Chapter 7*

"What *is* a Caucus-race?" said Alice; not that she much wanted to know . . .

"Why," said the Dodo, "the best way to explain it is to do it."

*Wonderland, Chapter 3*

The players all played at once without waiting for turns, quarrelling all the while, and fighting for hedgehogs.

*Wonderland, Chapter 8*

It was very like having a game of play with a cart-horse.

*Wonderland, Chapter 4*

"Un-dish-cover the fish, or dishcover the riddle."

*Looking-Glass, Chapter 9*

"Begin at the beginning,"
the King said, gravely,
"and go on till you come
to the end: then stop."

*Wonderland, Chapter 12*